THE TOP TEN CHRISTMAS SONGS **TO PLAY** ON PIANO

WISE PUBLICATIONS
part of The Music Sales Group
London / New York / Paris / Sydney / Copenhagen / Berlin / Madrid / Hong Kong / Tokyo

Published by
Wise Publications
14-15 Berners Street,
London W1T 3LJ, UK.

Exclusive Distributors:
Music Sales Limited
Distribution Centre, Newmarket Road,
Bury St Edmunds, Suffolk IP33 3YB, UK.
Music Sales Corporation
180 Madison Avenue, 24th Floor,
New York NY 10016, USA.
Music Sales Pty Limited
Level 4, Lisgar House,
30-32 Carrington Street,
Sydney, NSW 2000 Australia.

Order No. AM1012484
ISBN 978-1-78558-428-2

Compiled by Naomi Cook.
Notes written by Greg Johnson.

Photos courtesy of:
Page 1: James Devaney/WireImage
Page 13: Mike Coppola/Getty Images
Page 20: Warner Brothers/Getty Images
Page 25: GAB Archive/Redferns
Page 29: Gijsbert Hanekroot/Redferns
Page 35: Michael Ochs Archives/Getty Images
Page 40: Archive Photos/Getty Images
Page 47: Illustration by Raymond Briggs reproduced by permission Snowman Enterprises Ltd.
Page 55: Keystone/Getty Images
Page 59: GAB Archive/Redferns

Printed in the EU.

Your Guarantee of Quality
As publishers, we strive to produce every book to the
highest commercial standards.
This book has been carefully designed to minimise awkward
page turns and to make playing from it a real pleasure.
Particular care has been given to specifying acid-free, neutral-sized paper
made from pulps which have not been elemental chlorine bleached.
This pulp is from farmed sustainable forests and was
produced with special regard for the environment.
Throughout, the printing and binding have been planned to
ensure a sturdy, attractive publication which should give years of enjoyment.
If your copy fails to meet our high standards,
please inform us and we will gladly replace it.

www.musicsales.com

THE TOP TEN CHRISTMAS SONGS **TO** **PLAY** ON PIANO

Is there anything more heart-warming than the image of family and friends crowding around the piano to sing their favourite Christmas songs? We think not, so we've put together a collection of the best-loved Christmas hits to help you spread some Christmas cheer.

Covering everything from Bing Crosby's dreamy 'White Christmas' to the beautiful 'Walking In The Air' from The Snowman to party favourites such as Slade's 'Merry Xmas Everybody' and Mariah Carey's 'All I Want For Christmas Is You' – these are the cream of the (Christmas) crop. So round up the troops and get playing!

ALL I WANT FOR CHRISTMAS IS YOU

ARTIST: Mariah Carey
RELEASED: 1994

No Christmas playlist would be complete without Mariah Carey's modern classic. The familiar drawn-out opening phrases are full of anticipation, showcasing Carey's stunning voice at the height of her career, and when the piano triplets signal the new up-tempo beat that characterizes the rest of the song it's hard not to feel a little bit of excitement – even though many of us have heard the song hundreds, if not thousands, of times before!

Composed by Carey and her long-time collaborator, Grammy-winning record producer and songwriter Walter Afanasieff, the pair were initially sceptical about writing a Christmas album – Carey was a star at her peak, while the majority of artists making festive releases at the time were on the other side of their careers – but they eventually decided to go ahead with the project. A wise decision, as 'All I Want For Christmas Is You' became a massive smash hit and remains one of the most successful records ever released. Through this song and its accompanying album, *Merry Christmas*, Carey became the model for others to follow, inspiring a new generation of musicians and singers at the height of their fame to create their own Christmas hits.

ALL I WANT FOR CHRISTMAS IS YOU

Words & Music by Mariah Carey & Walter Afanasieff

9

10

11

12

FAIRYTALE OF NEW YORK

ARTIST: The Pogues feat. Kirsty MacColl

RELEASED: 1987

According to myth and legend, The Pogues' festive hit *Fairytale Of New York* came about after their frontman, Shane MacGowen, became determined to win a wager with Elvis Costello, who bet that the band would never be able to write a Christmas song. Emboldened by the challenge, they set about their task, although it took over two years before they could answer to the gauntlet thrown down by their friend and former producer.

Penned by MacGowen and the group's banjo player, Jem Fliner, the finished track was a duet based on a fictional couple at Christmas.

MacGowen took on the male character while English singer-songwriter Kirsty MacColl guested on the female part. Their chemistry and lively, raucous performances along with the cheeky lyrics made for a winning combination and the song soon became synonymous with ringing in the festive cheer and is now widely regarded as one of the greatest Christmas anthems of all time. The iconic piano intro is guaranteed to prompt a slurring singalong – see how many people can get their tongues around the lyrics when the rhythm picks up!

FAIRYTALE OF NEW YORK

Words & Music by Shane MacGowan & Jem Finer

kissed on the cor - ner, then danced through the night.__ *(Both)* The boys of the N. Y.
Christ-mas your arse!__ I pray God it's our last.

P. D. choir_ were sing-ing,__ 'Gal-way Bay'. And the bells_ were ring-ing out_

_ for Christ-mas Day.__

(Female) 5. You're a

HAVE YOURSELF A MERRY LITTLE CHRISTMAS

ARTIST: Frank Sinatra
RELEASED: 1957

This heart-warming ballad automatically conjures up festive images of people gathered around an open fire, stirring a rush of sentimentality and inviting the listener to take a moment to reflect and think about loved ones. Written by composers Hugh Martin and Ralph Blane, it was originally performed by Judy Garland in the 1944 musical *Meet Me In St. Louis*, yet it is Frank Sinatra's reworking of the track that became the definitive version, with a couple of changes to the lyrics and the unforgettable vocal delivery of the singer known to many simply as 'The Voice'.

With the tune set to feature on his 1957 album *A Jolly Christmas*, Ol' Blue Eyes asked Hugh Martin to inject a touch more positivity into the original, slightly melancholic lyrics in order to match the upbeat tone of the record. He also altered the focus to place more emphasis on celebrating the time of year rather than hoping for a better future. Both the album and the song became great successes, and welcome additions to the Christmas popular music canon.

HAVE YOURSELF A
MERRY LITTLE CHRISTMAS

Words & Music by Hugh Martin & Ralph Blane

merry lit-tle Christ-mas, make the Yule-tide gay.

From now on our trou-bles will be miles a-way.

Here we are as in old-en days, hap-py

gold-en days of yore. Faith-ful friends who are

JINGLE BELL ROCK

ARTIST: Bobby Helms
RELEASED: 1957

A firm fixture on festive track lists at radio stations across the USA ever since its release in 1957, 'Jingle Bell Rock' remains one of the most recognisable and memorable Christmas songs in the repertoire. It gained so much cultural recognition as a festive staple that it featured prominently in major films such as *Lethal Weapon* and *Home Alone 2: Lost in New York* and has been covered and re-released by numerous bands and artists.

The original version was recorded by Bobby Helms but its two writers worked outside of the music industry: Joseph Carleton Beal and James Ross Boothe had jobs in public relations and advertising respectively. Perhaps the most famous cover version of the song is the one recorded by Bill Haley & His Comets in 1968, which went missing for almost three decades until its eventual release in the 1990s. Its belated reappearance didn't stop it from becoming immensely popular, with its surf rock sound and steady, swinging laid back rhythm.

JINGLE BELL ROCK

Words & Music by Joseph Beal & James Boothe

to go glid - in' in a one-horse sleigh.__ Gid - dy - up, jin - gle horse,

pick up your feet,__ jin - gle a - round the clock. Mix and min - gle in a

jin - gl - in' beat,__ that's the jin - gle bell rock.

1.

2.

that's the jin - gle bell, that's the jin - gle bell rock._____

28

MERRY XMAS EVERYBODY

ARTIST: Slade
RELEASED: 1973

Famously recorded inside a sweltering New York studio on one of the hottest days of the year, Slade's 'Merry Xmas Everybody' overcame all obstacles and reached the Christmas No. 1 spot in 1973. The conditions could hardly have been less in tune with the Christmas spirit that the band were hoping to imbue the track with. Coming off their tour of the USA to hit the studio, they were still working under the pressures and moods of a band on the road, no one ready to settle down and write a definitive festive hit. Thankfully, frontman Noddy Holder had already written

the music and lyrics months before using an old tune from a previous band. He wanted to create something to cheer up the UK after a hard year of economic collapse and industrial action and 'Merry Xmas Everybody' was the result.

The bouncy shuffle rhythm, soaring chorus melody and positive lyrics make this festive favourite a joy to play and sing – use the left hand octave figures to recreate the jaunty feel of the band parts… and don't forget to yell 'It's Christmas!' at the end!

MERRY XMAS EVERYBODY

Words & Music by Neville Holder & James Lea

Does he ride___ a red-nosed rein-deer? Does a ton-up on___ his sleigh?___ Do the fair-ies keep him so-ber for___ a day?_____ So here it is: mer-ry Christ-mas, ev-'ry-bod-y's hav-ing fun.___

To Coda

Look to the fu - ture now_ it's on - ly just be -

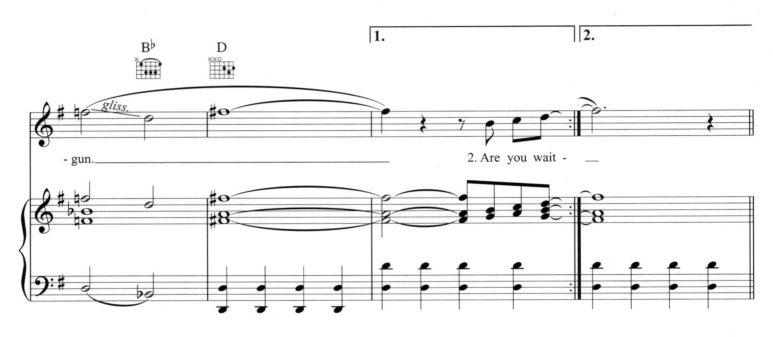

1. **2.**

- gun._____ 2. Are you wait -

What will your dad - dy do_____ when he sees your ma - ma kiss - in' San -

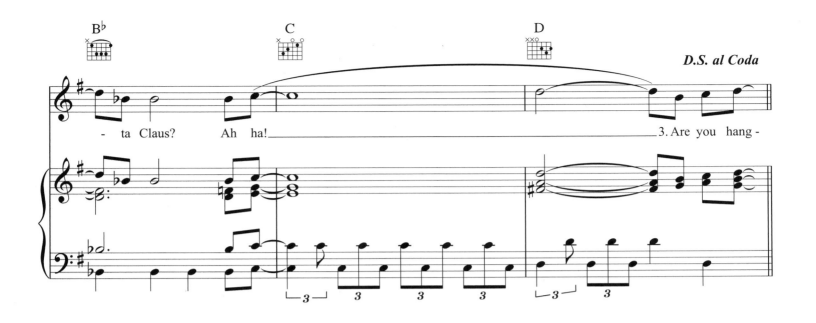

D.S. al Coda

- ta Claus? Ah ha! _____ 3. Are you hang-

is: mer - ry Christ - mas, ev - 'ry-bod - y's hav-ing fun.__

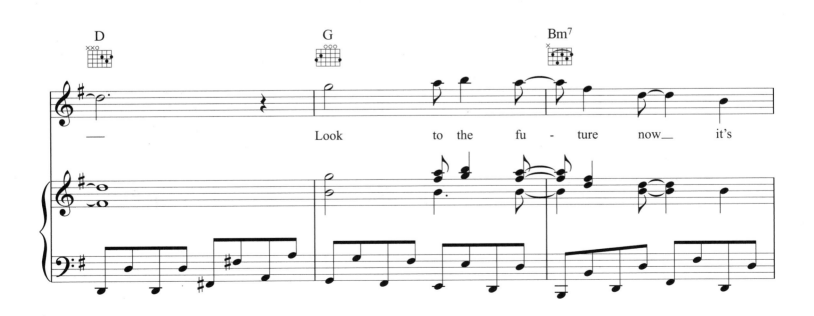

Look to the fu - ture now__ it's

Verse 2:
Are you waiting for the family to arrive?
Are you sure you got the room to spare inside?
Does your granny always tell you that the old songs are the best?
Then she's up and rock 'n' rolling with the rest!

Verse 3:
Are you hanging up a stocking on your wall?
Are you hoping that the snow will start to fall?
Do you ride on down the hillside in a buggy you have made?
When you land upon your head, then you've been slayed!

SANTA BABY

ARTIST: Eartha Kitt
RELEASED: 1953

Written by Joan Javits and Philip Springer as a send-up of a child's Christmas wish list to Santa Claus, the lyrics to 'Santa Baby' feature a woman desperate for jolly old Saint Nic to bring her luxury items from her favourite department store, boutiques and beyond. First performed in 1953 by Eartha Kitt, who said it was one of her favourite songs to record, it became a near-instant hit upon its release and Kitt would later record the tune twice more, heading into the studio with a more up-tempo version in 1963 after failing to make any impact with her second attempt in 1954 under a different title, 'This Year's Santa Baby'.

It has since become something of a standard, performed and covered by a whole range of artists, from Madonna and Kylie Minogue to Michael Buble and the cast of *Glee*. Cheeky, fun and a bit mischievous, 'Santa Baby' is – like the traditional, boozy Christmas trifle – fun and light-hearted, possessing just a touch of something slightly satirical for its grown-up audience to catch on to. Musically, too, it's a mix of knowing winks and slightly absurd juxtapositions played for laughs, and the original accompaniment translates really well to piano so you can bring out the humour of the composition in your own rendition.

SANTA BABY

Words & Music by Joan Javits, Phil Springer & Tony Springer

SANTA CLAUS IS COMIN' TO TOWN

ARTIST: Eddie Cantor
RELEASED: 1934

A Christmas hit for Eddie Cantor in 1934, 'Santa Claus Is Comin' To Town' sold over 100,000 copies of sheet music and more than 30,000 records in its first 24 hours – not bad in an age before CD singles, let alone digital downloads! Written by John Frederick Coots and Haven Gillespie, it has been covered numerous times since its first release, by artists as diverse as Michael Jackson and The Jackson 5, Frank Sinatra, The Beach Boys and even Dolly Parton.

The original version may be very much 'of its time' but one of the track's greatest strengths as a Christmas classic is its openness to reinterpretation. Sitting at the keys, it's easy to hear how so many artists have taken the raw materials of the tune and spun it in their own direction. Once learned, it's a fun song to play around with and tweak to suit your own interests and ideas. It's the Christmas gift that just keeps on giving!

SANTA CLAUS IS COMIN' TO TOWN

Words by Haven Gillespie
Music by J. Fred Coots

WALKING IN THE AIR
THEME FROM *THE SNOWMAN*

ARTIST: Peter Auty/Aled Jones
RELEASED: 1982

The Snowman was originally a children's book without words, written by Raymond Briggs and released in 1978. In 1982 the animated television special was broadcast, which featured music scored by Howard Blake. Entitled 'Walking In The Air (Theme from *The Snowman*)', the song was the main focus of the film, soundtracking the titular hero and the human child he befriends as they fly over the English countryside to reach a special Christmas party with Santa Claus and other snowy creatures. Other than this one piece, the film is, like the book, wordless.

It's often believed that former choirboy Aled Jones provided the vocals for the original version, but it was in fact Peter Auty who sung for Blake in 1982. Jones performed on a later version recorded after Auty's voice had broken. The piano part for the piece is almost as iconic as the melody, the repeated arpeggiated sequence creating a lilting, dreamy effect that reinforces the magical events in the film.

WALKING IN THE AIR
THEME FROM *THE SNOWMAN*

Words & Music by Howard Blake

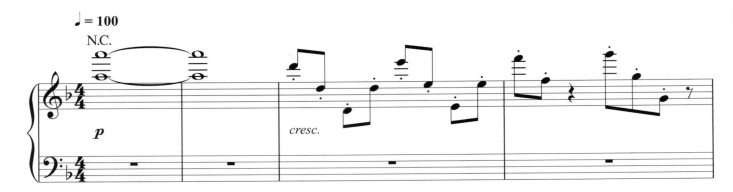

sleep-ing as we fly._____ I'm

hold-ing ve - ry tight,_____ I'm rid-ing in the mid - night

blue._____ I'm find-ing I can fly so

high a-bove with you._____

WHITE CHRISTMAS

ARTIST: Bing Crosby
RELEASED: 1942

Written by the legendary composer and songwriter, Irving Berlin, 'White Christmas' has become a true standard of the festive genre, performed and covered by an extensive list of stars and mainstream artists over the decades since its first release in 1942. However, it is Bing Crosby's performance that is by far and away the most definitive version of this Christmas classic, despite the fact that Crosby apparently failed to see anything special in the track at first. Recorded in May of that same year, and again for another release in March 1947, it remains the biggest-selling single of all time. As of 2016, it is believed to have sold in excess of 100 million records.

The song has a similar effect to Sinatra's 'Have Yourself A Merry Little Christmas' – it's easy to imagine any room turning into a cosy Christmas retreat, with snow on the windows, a log fire at your side and friends and family nearby. Perhaps it is the natural imagery and associations the song conjures that has made it such a beloved and widely-performed seasonal classic.

WHITE CHRISTMAS

Words & Music by Irving Berlin

The sun is shin-ing, the grass is green,_ the or-ange and palm trees sway. There's never been such a day in Bev-er-ly Hills, L. A.

WINTER WONDERLAND

ARTIST: Dean Martin
RELEASED: 1934

Like many songs in this collection, this tune has been performed and recorded by hundreds of musicians, with notable versions having been released by the likes of Dean Martin, Perry Como, Aretha Franklin and The Eurythmics.

Given the lack of specific reference to the Christian festival, 'Winter Wonderland' is technically classed – and this may or may not surprise you – as a winter song. But regardless of its genre affiliations, Felix Bernard and Richard B. Smith's 1934 creation is an undoubted festive favourite, with lyrical references to sleigh bells, snow, tweeting birds and the season of glad tidings and goodwill. The laid-back swing rhythm and lingering phrases somehow embody the holiday spirit. So, we may be breaking the rules a bit here, but we simply couldn't leave this easy-going seasonal classic out of our 'top ten'!

WINTER WONDERLAND

Words by Richard Smith
Music by Felix Bernard

O-ver the ground_ lies a man-tle of white,_ a hea-ven of dia-monds shine down through the night,_

two hearts are thrill - in' in spite of the chill_ in the weath - er.

Love knows no sea - son, love knows no clime,_ ro-mance can blos - som an - y old time,_

here in the o - pen, we're walk-in' and hop - in' to - geth - er!_____ Sleigh bells

ring, are you list - 'nin'? In the lane snow is glist - 'nin', a

then pre-tend that he is Par-son Brown._____ He'll say 'Are you mar-ried?' We'll say,

'No man! But you can do the job when you're in town!' Lat-er on we'll con-

-spire____ as we dream by the fire____ to face un-a-fraid,__ the

plans that we made,__ walk-in' in a win-ter won-der - land! Sleigh bells -land!

123456789

63

ALSO AVAILABLE...

THE TOP TEN CLASSICAL PIANO PIECES EVERY BEGINNER SHOULD LEARN	THE TOP TEN MOST BEAUTIFUL PIECES TO PLAY ON PIANO	THE TOP TEN CHRISTMAS SONGS TO PLAY ON PIANO	THE TOP TEN LOVE SONGS TO PLAY ON PIANO	THE TOP TEN PIANO SONGS OF ALL TIME
AM1012231	AM1012253	AM1012484	AM1012275	AM1012242

BERCEUSE *from Dolly Suite, Op. 56* FAURÉ	**ADAGIO FOR STRINGS** BARBER	**ALL I WANT FOR CHRISTMAS IS YOU** MARIAH CAREY	**AT LAST** ETTA JAMES	**BRIDGE OVER TROUBLED WATER** SIMON & GARFUNKEL
THE DOLL'S COMPLAINT FRANCVK	**ANDANTE GRAZIOSO** Theme from *Piano Sonata No. 11 In A Major*, K331 MOZART	**FAIRYTALE OF NEW YORK** THE POGUES FEAT. KIRSTY MacCOLL	**CLOSE TO YOU (THEY LONG TO BE)** THE CARPENTERS	**CLOCKS** COLDPLAY
FÜR ELISE BEETHOVEN	**CLAIR DE LUNE** No. 3 from *Suite Bergamasque* DEBUSSY	**HAVE YOURSELF A MERRY LITTLE CHRISTMAS** FRANK SINATRA	**(EVERYTHING I DO) I DO IT FOR YOU** BRYAN ADAMS	**DON'T STOP BELIEVIN'** JOURNEY
FUGUE *from Five Miniature Preludes And Fugues* ROWLEY	**LASCIA CH'IO PIANGA** *from Rinaldo*, HWV 7 HANDEL	**JINGLE BELL ROCK** BOBBY HELMS	**THE FIRST TIME EVER I SAW YOUR FACE** ROBERTA FLACK	**LIFE ON MARS?** DAVID BOWIE
PAVANE DE LA BELLE AU BOIS DORMANT *from Ma Mère L'Oye* RAVEL	**MISERERE** ALLEGRI	**MERRY XMAS EVERYBODY** SLADE	**HOW DEEP IS YOUR LOVE** BEE GEES	**ORDINARY PEOPLE** JOHN LEGEND
MELODIE *from Album Für Die Jugend* SCHUMANN	**MOONLIGHT SONATA, OP. 27, NO. 2** BEETHOVEN	**SANTA BABY** EARTHA KITT	**I WILL ALWAYS LOVE YOU** WHITNEY HOUSTON	**SKINNY LOVE** BIRDY
MINUET IN F MAJOR, K2 MOZART	**NIMROD** *from Enigma Variations,* Op. 36 ELGAR	**SANTA CLAUS IS COMIN' TO TOWN** EDDIE CANTOR	**MAKE YOU FEEL MY LOVE** ADELE	**SOMEONE LIKE YOU** ADELE
PRELUDE NO. 1 IN C MAJOR, BWV 846 BACH	**NOCTURNE IN E♭ MAJOR, OP. 9, NO. 2** CHOPIN	**WALKING IN THE AIR** Theme from *The Snowman* PETER AUTY/ALED JONES	**MY HEART WILL GO ON** *from Titanic* CÉLINE DION	**SOMEWHERE ONLY WE KNOW** KEANE
SARABANDE *from Keyboard Suite In D minor*, HWV 437 HANDEL	**NUVOLE BIANCHE** EINAUDI	**WHITE CHRISTMAS** BING CROSBY	**MY IMMORTAL** EVANESCENCE	**A THOUSAND MILES** VANESSA CARLTON
SARABANDE EINAUDI	**ON THE NATURE OF DAYLIGHT/ WRITTEN ON THE SKY** *from Shutter Island* RICHTER	**WINTER WONDERLAND** DEAN MARTIN	**YOUR SONG** ELTON JOHN	**TINY DANCER** ELTON JOHN

  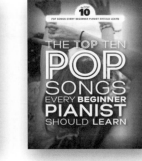 

AM1012286	AM1012319	AM1012264	AM1012297	AM1012308